EDGAR ALLAN POE

Raintree is an imprint of Capstone
Global Library Limited, a company
incorporated in England and Wales
having its registered office at 7 Pilgrim
Street, London, EC4V 6LB -- Registered
company number: 6695582

www.raintreepublishers.co.uk
myorders@raintreepublishers.co.uk

ISBN 978 1 406 26645 0
18 17 16 15 14 13
10 9 8 7 6 5 4 3 2 1

British Library Cataloguing in Publication Data
A full catalogue record for this book is available from the British Library.

Summary: Sentenced to death by the Inquisition, a desperate man awaits his fate locked in a dark
dungeon. There's a bottomless pit below him. A razor sharp pendulum swings from above. Hideous
demons are carved into the metal walls. The man's only companions are beady-eyed rats and the echo
of his own terrified voice. When the demons start to smile, he begins to wonder if he has lost his
mind...

Art Director: Bob Lentz
Graphic Designer: Hilary Wacholz
Edited by Diyan Leake
Production by Victoria Fitzgerald
Printed in China by Leo Paper Products Ltd

THE PIT AND THE PENDULUM

BY EDGAR ALLAN POE

RETOLD BY SEAN TULIEN

ILLUSTRATED BY J.C. FABUL

Here a wicked mob of torturers long fed their undying thirst for innocent blood. Now that the homeland is saved, and the cave of murder is destroyed, life and health appear where grim death once was...

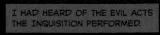

I HAD HEARD OF THE EVIL ACTS THE INQUISITION PERFORMED.

THEY USED TORTURE TO GET THE ANSWERS THEY WANTED.

...AND THEN THEY EXECUTED THEIR PRISONERS.

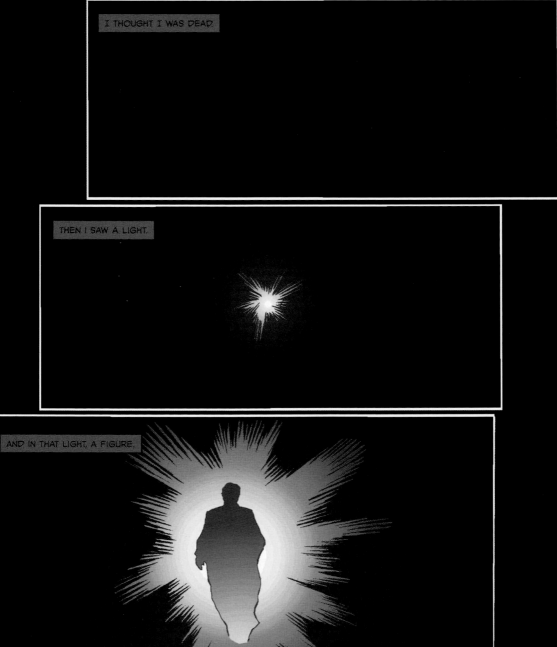

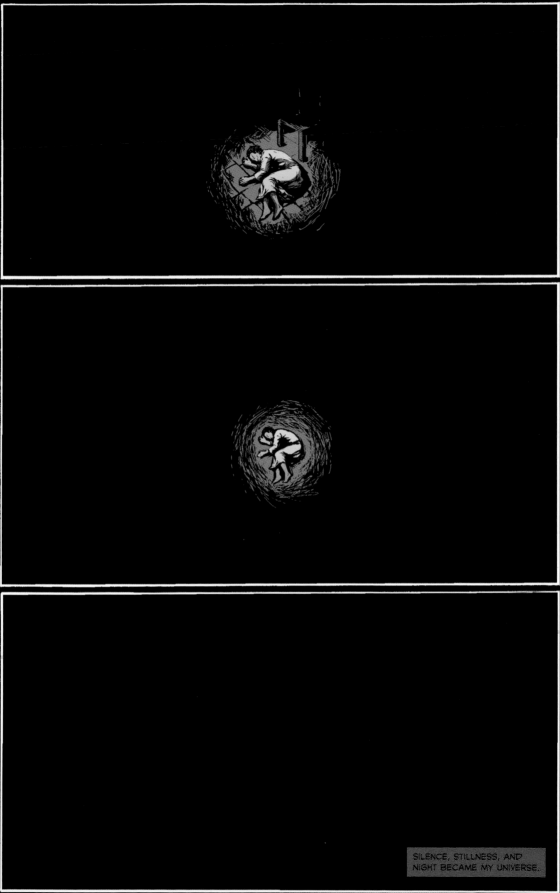

SILENCE, STILLNESS, AND
NIGHT BECAME MY UNIVERSE.

THEN, VERY SUDDENLY, THERE CAME TO ME A MOTION AND A SOUND.

I AWOKE IN A STRANGE PLACE.

THA-THUMP!!

THA-THUMP!!

I DIDN'T DARE OPEN MY EYES.

THE ATMOSPHERE FELT INTOLERABLY CLOSE.

I STRUGGLED TO BREATHE.

I TRIED TO REMEMBER THE INQUISITORIAL PROCEEDINGS, HOPING IT WOULD HELP ME DETERMINE MY CURRENT LOCATION.

BUT MY MEMORIES, POLLUTED BY FEAR, SEEMED MORE LIKE NIGHTMARES.

THOSE SENTENCED TO DEATH BY THE INQUISITION WERE BURNED AT THE STAKE. SO WHY WAS I HERE?

THEN A FEARFUL IDEA CAME TO MY MIND...

...HAD I BEEN BURIED ALIVE?

I DON'T KNOW HOW LONG I WAS OUT, BUT WHEN I CAME TO, I FOUND SOME BREAD AND A PITCHER OF WATER NEXT TO ME.

I WAS TOO HUNGRY TO WORRY ABOUT HOW IT GOT THERE.

I THEN RESUMED MY CIRCUIT AROUND THE PRISON.

AFTER A TIME, I CAME UPON THE FRAGMENT OF CLOTH.

I HAD COUNTED FIFTY-TWO PACES BEFORE I PASSED OUT, AND I HAD JUST NOW WALKED ANOTHER FORTY-EIGHT PACES AS I ARRIVED AT THE PIECE OF CLOTH.

THAT MEANT, IN ALL, THERE WERE A HUNDRED PACES AROUND THE ROOM.

MOVING AWAY FROM THE WALL, I DECIDED TO CROSS THE DUNGEON.

I HAD ADVANCED SOME TEN OR TWELVE PACES IN THIS MANNER WHEN THE PIECE OF TORN CLOTH FROM MY ROBE BECAME ENTANGLED BETWEEN MY LEGS.

RRRRRIP

WHAM!

AFTER THE CONFUSION OF MY FALL, I REALIZED SOMETHING...

I HAD FALLEN AT THE VERY EDGE OF A CIRCULAR PIT.

A STRANGE SMELL ROSE TO MY NOSTRILS LIKE THAT OF DECAYING FUNGUS.

GRASPING AT THE STONES JUST BELOW THE LIP, I SUCCEEDED IN DISLODGING A SMALL PIECE OF STONE.

HOW DEEP IS IT?

JUST THEN, A SOUND CAME FROM ABOVE ME LIKE THE RAPID OPENING AND CLOSING OF A DOOR.

A FAINT GLEAM OF LIGHT LIT UP PART OF THE GLOOM.

CLACK!

I NOW CLEARLY SAW THE DOOM THAT HAD BEEN PREPARED FOR ME.

THE INQUISITION WAS FORCING ME TO MAKE A CHOICE: STARVE, OR LEAP TO MY DEATH.

I GROPED MY WAY BACK TO THE WALL. STARVATION WAS PREFERABLE TO THAT PIT.

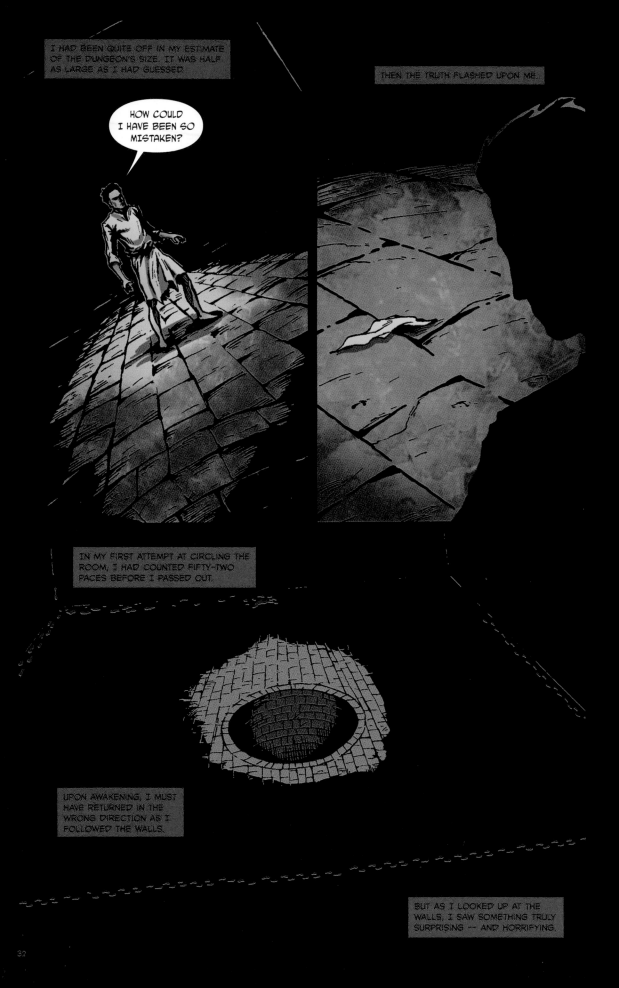

IT WAS THEN THAT I NOTICED A LOAF OF BREAD AND A PITCHER OF WATER NEXT TO ME.

I WAS CONSUMED BY THIRST, AND EMPTIED THE VESSEL IN A SINGLE GULP.

IT MUST HAVE BEEN DRUGGED, FOR I IMMEDIATELY FELL INTO A DEEP SLEEP.

A SLEEP OF DEATH, FILLED WITH NIGHTMARES AND AGONY.

WHEN I AWOKE, I DISCOVERED I HAD BEEN STRAPPED TO A FRAMEWORK OF WOOD.

I WAS SECURELY BOUND TO THE FRAME BY A LONG STRAP.

IT PASSED AROUND MY LIMBS AND BODY MANY TIMES, LEAVING ONLY MY HEAD AND MY LEFT ARM FREE.

I COULD SUPPLY MYSELF WITH FOOD FROM A DISH WHICH LAY BY MY SIDE ON THE FLOOR.

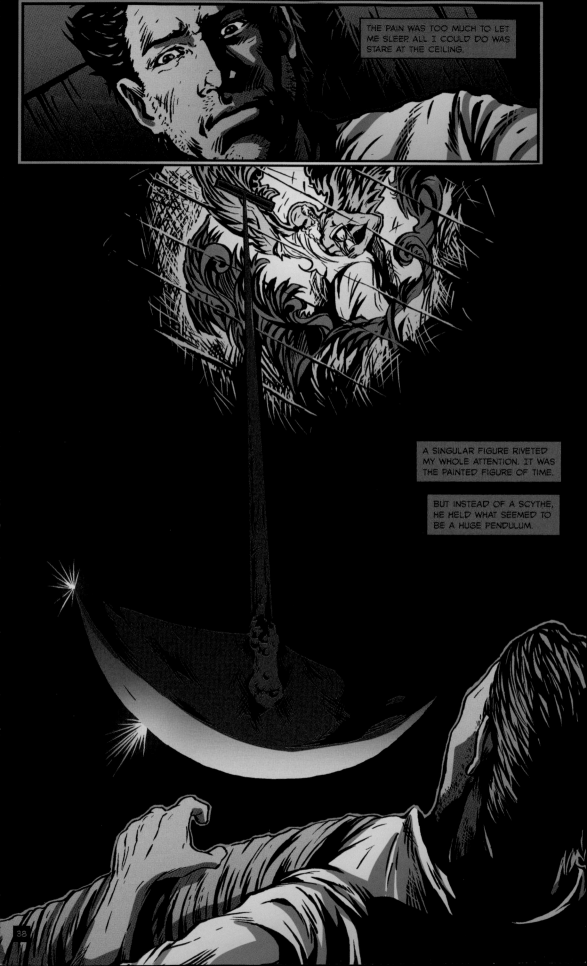

THE PAIN WAS TOO MUCH TO LET ME SLEEP ALL I COULD DO WAS STARE AT THE CEILING.

A SINGULAR FIGURE RIVETED MY WHOLE ATTENTION. IT WAS THE PAINTED FIGURE OF TIME.

BUT INSTEAD OF A SCYTHE, HE HELD WHAT SEEMED TO BE A HUGE PENDULUM.

...AND SAW SOMETHING STARING BACK AT ME.

SEVERAL SOMETHINGS.

THEY CAME UP HURRIEDLY TOWARD THE SCENT OF THE MEAT.

I STRUGGLED TO FREE MYSELF.

BUT, ALAS, I COULD NOT, AND IN TEN OR TWELVE MORE SWINGS, THE STEEL BLADE WOULD SLICE INTO MY CHEST AND KILL ME -- SLOWLY.

THE BEADY EYES OF A RAT STILL STARED AT ME FROM THE DARKNESS.

THE VERMIN HAD EATEN ALL BUT A SMALL BIT OF FOOD FROM MY DISH.

THEY HAD EVEN BIT INTO MY FINGER AS I SCARED THEM AWAY.

WOULD THEY FEED ON ME AFTER THE PENDULUM ENDED MY LIFE...?

SUDDENLY, A DESPERATE IDEA SPRANG TO MY MIND.

I THEN LAY BREATHLESSLY STILL.

ONE OR TWO OF THE BOLDEST RATS LEAPED UPON THE FRAMEWORK AND NIBBLED AT THE STRAP.

FIERY DEMONS GLARED AT ME FROM ALL DIRECTIONS.

I SAW IT NOW, WHAT THE INQUISITION HAD PLANNED FOR ME. I HAD ESCAPED THE PENDULUM ONLY TO FACE A WORSE FATE...

...THEY WOULD BURN ME ALIVE, AFTER ALL.

THE HEAT WAS TERRIBLE. I FELT MY SKIN BEGIN TO BLISTER.

THEN I NOTICED A LOW, RUMBLING SOUND COMING FROM ALL AROUND ME.

KRRRSSH

AS I GLANCED AT THE WALLS...

RRRSSSH

...I REALIZED TWO OF THE WALL ANGLES WERE EXPANDING, AND TWO OF THE IRON WALLS WERE SHRINKING.

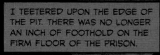

I TEETERED UPON THE EDGE OF THE PIT. THERE WAS NO LONGER AN INCH OF FOOTHOLD ON THE FIRM FLOOR OF THE PRISON.

THE AGONY OF MY SOUL FOUND VENT IN ONE LOUD, LONG, AND FINAL SCREAM OF DESPAIR.

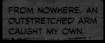

Over the course of his life, Edgar Allan Poe submitted many stories and poems to a number of publications. Either they were rejected, or he received little or no compensation for them. His most popular work, "The Raven", quite nearly made him a household name -- but only earned him nine dollars.

Poe was unable to hold a single job for very long, jumping from position to position for most of his life. He had very few friends, was in constant financial trouble, and struggled with alcoholism throughout his adult years. Edgar's family rarely helped him during these difficult times. In fact, when Edgar's father died in 1834, he did not even mention Edgar in his will.

Though largely unappreciated in his own lifetime, Edgar Allan Poe is now recognized as one of the most important writers of literature in English.

THE RETELLING AUTHOR

SEAN TULIEN is a children's book editor living and working in Minnesota, USA. In his spare time, he likes to read, eat sushi, ride his mountain bike, listen to loud music, watch unsettling movies, and write books like this one.

THE ILLUSTRATOR

J.C. FABUL grew up in Palawan, Philippines, and now lives in Manila. He studied Fine Arts in college, earning a degree in Painting. Illustrating comics is a big part of his life, but he also does digital illustration, portraiture, art commissions, and sketch cards.

GLOSSARY

ABYSS very deep hole that seems to have no bottom

AGONY great pain or suffering

CIRCUIT journey beginning and ending in the same spot

DECAYING rotting or breaking down of plant or animal matter by natural causes

DESPAIR lose hope completely

DREADFUL very frightening, awful, or bad

ETERNAL lasting forever

HIDEOUS ugly or horrible

INQUISITION official investigation of a political or religious nature that was known for violating individual rights, prejudice on the part of the judges, and cruel punishments

LOCUTION speech or verbal expression

REJOICE happily celebrate

RELIEF· feeling of freedom from pain or worry

WRITHE twist and turn, as if in pain

VISUAL QUESTIONS

1. The Inquisition intended to make the Narrator's imprisonment as unpleasant as possible. Look through this book and find several examples of ways they made the Narrator suffer.

2. The Narrator goes through a series of different emotions on pages 46–47. For each panel, describe the emotion you think the Narrator is feeling based on the captions, colour, and the illustrations.

3. Why do you think Poe included a painting of Time, or Father Time, on the ceiling of the dungeon? [Page 38.]

4. The Narrator has a few nightmares or hallucinations in this book. Explain how the nightmares or hallucinations are related to his experiences.

5. Identify several panels in this book where fear twisted the Narrator's memories, thoughts, or perspective.

6. The final panel in this book [page 63] shows the Narrator set against a white background. How does it differ from the rest of the book? Why do you think the panel is illustrated in this way?

THE FALL OF THE
HOUSE OF USHER

WHILE MY COMPANIONSHIP DID SEEM TO HELP HIM A LITTLE...

...RODERICK'S SICKNESS WAS PROVING TO BE...

...INFECTIOUS.